STAY AWHILE

SCRIBNER READING SERIES

STAY AWHILE

Jack Cassidy

Doris Roettger   *Karen K. Wixson*

SCRIBNER EDUCATIONAL PUBLISHERS
New York

ACKNOWLEDGMENTS
Portions of this text have been adapted from materials
originally prepared under the direction of Charles Walcutt
and Dr. Glenn McCracken.
"Sleeping Outdoors" from RHYMES ABOUT US by Marchette Chute.
Copyright © 1974 by Marchette Chute. Reprinted by permission of
the publisher, E.P. Dutton, a division of New American Library and
the author.
"Rocks" by Florence Parry Heide. Copyright Florence Parry Heide and
reprinted by permission of the author.

ILLUSTRATIONS:
Cover: Cheryl Griesbach & Stanley Martucci.
Francoise Amadieu 98-105; Yvette Banek 35-41; Alex Bloch 64-71;
Jan Brett 92-97, 116-117; Rick Brown 171-178; Bill Colrus 50-56;
Jack E. Davis 140-141; Carol Inouye 8-9, 62-63, 82-83, 84-91, 120-121;
True Kelley 106-115; Alan Magee 170; David McPhail 10-34; Meredith
Nemirov 122-132; Victor Paniagua 162-169; Rodica Prato 179-187;
Roger Roth 72-81; Sally Springer 133-139, 142-148.

PHOTOGRAPHY:
42, 43, 48: Harold Hutchinson/Ackroyd Photography; 44: Cary
Wolinsky/Stock Boston; 45: Weyerhauser/Lowell Georgia/Photo
Researchers Inc.; 46: Bruce M. Wellman/Stock-Boston; 47: Calvin
Larsen/Photo Researchers Inc.; 50: R. Kinne—San Diego Zoo/Photo
Researchers Inc.; 51, 56: Emuce Harris/Photo Researchers Inc.; 52,
53, 55: Jerry Cooke/Animals-Animals; 57, 58, 59: Michal Heron; 86:
Robert Noonan/Photo Researchers Inc.; 88: J.H. Robinson/Photo
Researchers Inc.

SCRIBNER EDUCATIONAL PUBLISHERS
866 Third Avenue
New York, NY 10022
Collier Macmillan Publishers, London
Collier Macmillan Canada, Inc.

Printed in the United States of America
ISBN 0-20-256050-5
9 8 7 6 5 4 3 2 1

Contents

PETS AND TRICKS 1

The Trick

by David McPhail

Part 1: Ellen's Bad Luck

Ellen had a cat, Cuddles, and a dog, Rags. Ellen wanted her cat and dog to do a trick. Rags and Cuddles did not want to. They wanted to nap.

But Ellen still wanted to do the trick. Ellen helped Rags stand up on his back legs. She put Cuddles on top of Rags.

Cuddles did not want to sit on Rags. She kicked and struggled and fell on Ellen.

Ellen fell back and hit her leg
on the steps.

"Mom! Mom!" she called.

Rags barked and barked.
Cuddles ran under the steps.

Ellen's mom ran out. She saw
a big lump on Ellen's leg.

Ellen's mom ran in and called
for help.

At last a van from the hospital pulled in and stopped. Ellen was lifted up on a cot and put into the van. Ellen and her mom left for the hospital.

Cuddles and Rags wanted to see Ellen. They went to the hospital. Mrs. Wilson met Cuddles and Rags in the hall.

"Out! Out!" she said. "Animals are not allowed in the hospital!"

16

Long **a, a__e**

can—cane	at—ate	mad—made
tap—tape	past—paste	hat—hate

date	take	name	safe
late	lake	game	lane

plate	make	came	made
skate	snake	became	trade

The Trick

Part 2: Rags, Cuddles, and
Grandma

Rags was sad. "I miss Ellen,"
he said.

"I miss her, too," said
Cuddles. "But we can't get into
the hospital."

"Yes, we can," said Rags. "I
will show you how."

Rags ran up the steps to the
attic. Cuddles ran up after him.
Rags showed Cuddles a big trunk.
Rags pulled out a red dress and a
big hat. Cuddles pulled out a
black cane and brown glasses.

Rags put on the red dress. He held the cane in his front paw.

Cuddles put on the big hat and the glasses. She hopped up and sat on top of Rags.

Cuddles and Rags went to the hospital.

"I came to see Ellen Baker,"
Cuddles said to Mrs. Wilson. "I
am her grandma. I came to help
her get well."

"Me, too!" said Rags.

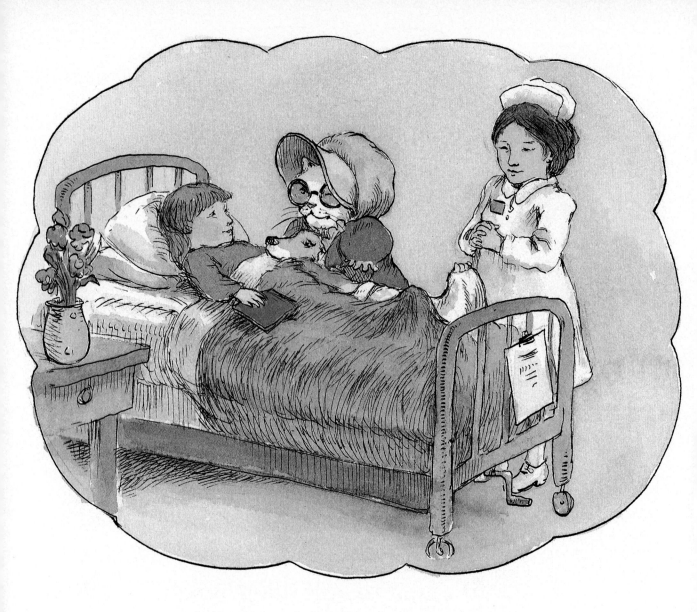

"Grandma came to see you,"
Mrs. Wilson said to Ellen.

"Grandma!" Ellen said.
"I'm glad you came!"

Ellen held out her arms and hugged Grandma. But Rags fell down, and Cuddles landed in Mrs. Wilson's arms.

"You are not Ellen's grandma!" said Mrs. Wilson. "You are the same cat and dog! Out you go!"

Rags ran down the hall.
Cuddles ran after him. Mrs. Wilson
ran after the dog and the cat.

Ellen saw it all from her bed.
She giggled and giggled. She felt a
lot better.

Ellen got better. Dr. Wade came in to see her.

"Ellen's leg is a lot better," Dr. Wade said.

"Can I go now?" asked Ellen.

"Yes, Dad and Mom can take you to the car," said Dr. Wade.

Cuddles and Rags ran to Ellen as she got out of the car. Cuddles rubbed on Ellen's cast. Rags barked and licked her hand.

Ellen was glad she was back, too.

CHECK FOR UNDERSTANDING

1. Who came to see Ellen in the hospital?

2. How did Rags and Cuddles get into the hospital?

are in **care**

care	dare	stare	scare
careful	dared	stared	scared

Hard Ice

TAKE CARE
SOFT ICE

It was winter. Ice was on the
lake. Otter got out his skates. He
got out his helmet and pads. He
put on his cape and mittens. He
held a red cane in his hand.

Otter was a careful skater. He
skated up and down the lake.

Skunk came to skate on the lake, too. She had no cape and no mittens. She did not put on a helmet and pads.

Skunk was a fast skater. She skated faster and faster. She wanted to show Otter how fast she was on the ice.

TAKE CARE
SOFT ICE

Skunk grinned. She waved as she skated past Otter.

Skunk didn't see the big flag on the left. The flag warned, "Take care! Soft ice!"

31

Skunk skated past the flag and fell into the lake. She struggled and struggled in the melted ice and water.

"HELP!" hollered Skunk. "I can't swim! I will drown!"

Skunk was scared.

TAKE CARE
SOFT ICE

Otter got down on the hard ice. He held out his cane to Skunk. She grabbed the cane, and Otter pulled her out.

Otter put his warm cape and mittens on Skunk.

"I am safe now, thanks to you," Skunk said.

"Didn't you see the flag?" asked Otter.

"No," said Skunk. "But from now on, I will take better care. I will still show off. But I will do it on hard ice!"

CHECK FOR UNDERSTANDING

1. Why did Skunk fall into the water?

2. How did Otter help Skunk?

long **e, E e**

he	we	remember
me	be	reward

long **e, ee**

see	need	deep	feel
tree	feed	keep	feet
free	weed	sleep	sweep
agree	week	asleep	street

Mr. Keenan's Contest

It was a summer day. Lee and his dad sat at the table. His dad had made him a game. Deke, Lee's pal, came up the steps. Lee's mom let Deke in.

"I went up the street to Mr. Keenan's Pet Market," Deke said. "He wants us to enter a pet contest."

Lee and Deke went to see Mr. Keenan.

"Yes," he said, "a contest will be held on Monday. Get a funny pet and you can enter it in the contest."

Lee and Deke agreed to get a funny pet for Mr. Keenan's contest.

Is a bee a funny pet? Is a bee that has big feet a funny pet? Is a tree frog a funny pet? Is a tree frog in a dress a funny pet?

Lee and Deke began to hunt for pets to enter in the contest.

Deke went up a tall tree to hunt for his funny pet. A robin in a nest was all he saw.

Lee went to the lake. One duck was all he saw. It swam in the water. It was not a funny pet.

Can they get funny pets? Will they be able to enter the contest?

It is Monday. A lot of funny
pets are at Mr. Keenan's Pet
Market. A brown beetle that
skates is in the contest. A rabbit
that hops on his back legs is in
the contest.

Deke has a snake that grins.
But Lee wins the contest. He has
a green grasshopper that winks!

CHECK FOR UNDERSTANDING

1. Why did Deke go to see Lee?

2. Where was the contest?

How Lumber Is Made

Pete's dad puts on a hard hat.
He starts his power saw. The saw
cuts deep into the trunk of a tree.
Pete's dad is a logger.

The big tree starts to fall.
Pete's dad warns the loggers to
keep back. BEWARE!

TIM-BER-R-R-R!

After a tree is cut and
trimmed, it is called a log. Big
claws pick up the logs. The logs
drop onto a truck. The truck
takes the logs to a sawmill.

At the sawmill, the logs are
dumped into a pond. Water keeps
the logs safe from insects.

In the mill, Pete's dad must
be careful. Big fast saws cut the
logs into lumber.

The wet lumber is put out in the sun.

After weeks in the sun, lumber can be made into beds, desks, and tables.

Pete wants to be a logger.
Pete's dad and mom agree. Pete
can be a logger if he wants to be.

CHECK FOR UNDERSTANDING

1. How is lumber made?

2. What can lumber be made
   into?

long **e, ea**

eat	sea	read	team
seat	seal	leap	treat
meat	meal	leaf	repeat

ea with **r**

near	ear	fear
dear	hear	clear

49

Slick the Seal

Slick is a big black seal. He is the star of a water show. Slick can swim fast. He can do stunts in the water.

April helps Slick do the stunts. April has a small clicker in her hand. After a stunt, April presses the clicker.

Cl--ick! The click tells Slick
he did his stunt well.

Slick hears the click. He
swims to April for his reward.
April gets a bit of cod from her
bucket. Slick leaps up for his
treat.

Crowds see the show. They sit in seats near the water.

April tells Slick to wave at the crowd. Slick stands on his flippers and waves. The crowd waves back.

April clicks the clicker. Slick
gets a reward. April rubs Slick
with her hand. A rub is a treat, too.

April wants a big kiss from
Slick. She stands near the water
and bends down.

April calls, "Slick, kiss me!"
Slick leaps up from the water and
kisses her.

"Arf! Arf!" he barks.

The crowd claps and claps.
The clicker clicks, and Slick gets
cod bits.

The last stunt is hard for
Slick. He swims to a tall tower.
His flippers help Slick go up the
tower. He gets to the top.

April calls, "Slick, do a back flip!" Slick leaps off the tower. His flippers go up, and he flips back. The crowd stands up and claps.

Slick hears the clicker. He gets a rub from April and waves to the crowd. Slick has ended the show.

CHECK FOR UNDERSTANDING

1. What tells Slick he did the stunt well?

2. What stunts can Slick do?

You Can Make It With Paper Plates

A Sea Beast

To make a sea beast you will need:
2 paper plates
strips of paper
markers, pens
stapler, paste

To make its ears:
1. Cut one paper plate into two parts.

2. Trim the parts a little to fit.

3. Staple the ears to the plate you did not cut.

To make its face:
4. Make a beak from scraps of paper plates. Tape the beak onto the face.

5. Add  and a
Make the sea beast as funny as you can.

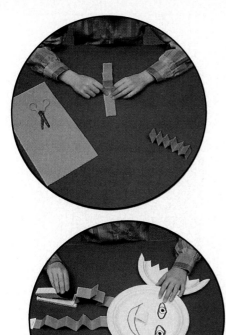

To make its legs:
6. Bend strips of paper to make legs. Paste the legs on.

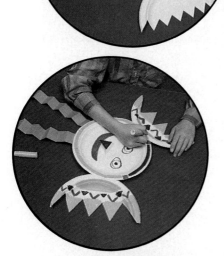

To make its feet:
7. Make two feet from the paper plate scraps. Staple the feet onto the ends of the legs.

8. Decorate the sea beast with markers.

9. Cut a rubber band and staple it onto the back. The sea beast will swim for you!

Who Said It?

1. "Slick, do a back flip!"

2. "I came to see Ellen Baker.
I am her grandma."

3. "Out! Out!
Animals are not allowed in the
hospital!"

D

E

F

4. "I am safe now, thanks to you."

5. "Get a funny pet and you can enter it in the contest."

6. "BEWARE! TIM-BER-R-R-R!"

LET'S GO OUTSIDE 2

Mr. H. Haines
15 Main Street
Red Rock, Texas 78662
U.S.A.

long **a, ai**

mail	tail	main
sail	trail	rain
nail	trailer	train
paid	wait	paint
afraid	waited	painted

ai with **r**

air	pair	stairs
airplane	hair	upstairs

The Lost Letter

Deena Lake takes the mail in the town of Red Rock. It is hard for Miss Lake to take the mail fast. It is hard to see the numbers.

The numbers need to be nailed up and painted black. One day Deena Lake had a problem.

Carlota and Carmen saw
Deena Lake. They ran down Main
Street to speak to her. Miss Lake
was glad to see Carlota and
Carmen.

"I need help," said Miss
Lake. "Here is a lost letter. It is
for a Mr. Haines. The address is
15 Main Street. I went up and
down Main Street, but I didn't
see number 15."

"I will help you," said Carlota.

"Wait, let me help, too," said Carmen.

Carmen held on to the mail cart. Carlota held Miss Lake's cap.

Carlota frowned. "Number 15, Main Street," she said to herself. "That must be in the park."

Carlota grabbed her sister's hand and started to run down a trail. It led to a big trailer park.

"Wait for me!" called Miss Lake.

Carmen and Carlota stopped in front of a trailer. Number 15 was painted on the trailer, but it was hard to see.

"Here they are!" called Carmen. "The numbers fell down into the flower bed."

They saw a man in back of the trailer. He held a can of paint. The man saw Miss Lake and came out in front.

"Are you Mr. Haines?" Miss Lake asked the man.

"Yes, I am," said the man.

"I have a letter for you," said Miss Lake.

The man grinned. "It's from Spain," he said. "I waited and waited for that letter. I was afraid it was lost."

"It was lost," said Miss Lake. "I didn't see the number 15, but Carlota and Carmen spotted it."

"I am glad they saw my number," said Mr. Haines. "I will put the numbers back up. I will paint the numbers black. I want you to see my number 15."

"Thank you, Mr. Haines," said Miss Lake. "From now on, I will see that letters to you do not get lost."

CHECK FOR UNDERSTANDING

1. Why was it hard for Miss Lake to take the mail fast?

2. How did Carlota and Carmen help Deena Lake?

Ben and the Tent

It was late summer. Craig and Carl rested near a tent on Craig's back lawn. Craig and Carl were ten. They had slept in the tent all week.

Ben ran across the lawn. Ben was six. He had not slept in the tent at all.

"Ben," said Craig, "I dare you. I dare you to sleep in the tent with us."

Ben waited. He was scared, but he said, "OK, I will."

Ben went upstairs to see his mom.

"Mom," he said, "can I sleep in the tent with Craig and Carl?"

"Yes, dear," his mom said. "But it will get dark. Will you be afraid?"

"No," said Ben. "I will be OK. If I do get scared, Craig and Carl can take care of me."

"OK," said his mom. "Take a blanket and Dad's cot with you."

Ben put on a pair of warm-up pants and a top. In his left arm he held a lantern and cans of lemonade. On his back he had the blanket. With his free arm, Ben dragged Dad's cot.

Craig and Carl helped Ben set up the cot. They ate peanuts and sipped lemonade. After dark, they made up a game in the glare of the lantern.

It began to get late and they got into bed.

Tap, tap. Tap, tap, tap.

"Is that a bear?" called Ben.

"No," said Carl as he got out of bed. "It has started to rain."

Carl pulled the tent flaps in. "Now it will not rain in here," he said.

"Will we see a bear?" asked Ben.

"Bears do not wander on back lawns," Carl said. "But if they do, Craig has bells that scare bears."

A wind began to rattle the trees. Ben was afraid.

"Are you scared?" he asked Craig.

"I'm ten," said Craig. "I'm not scared to sleep in the tent now."

A wind rattled the trees again. A clump, clump came near the tent. Carl hopped up and put his ear to the tent's flap.

"Do you hear that clump, clump?" asked Carl.

"It's a bear!" he screamed. "Craig, get the bells!"

The clump, clump came nearer and nearer. Craig and Carl got under Ben's cot and waited. Ben hid his face under the blanket.

The tent flaps were pulled back. The big bear came in! The *bear* was Ben's dad!

"I came in to see if you three are OK," Ben's dad said.

"We are now," said Ben with a grin.

CHECK FOR UNDERSTANDING

1. Why did Ben sleep in the tent?

2. What scared Ben, Craig, and Carl?

Sleeping Outdoors

by Marchette Chute

Under the dark is a star,
Under the star is a tree,
Under the tree is a blanket,
And under the blanket is me.

83

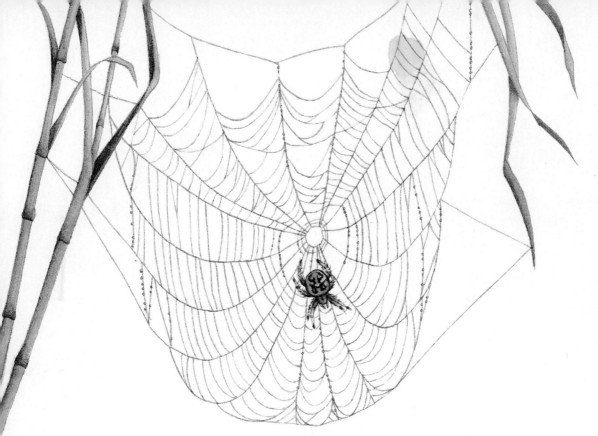

long **i**, **I i**

I am	find	spider
I'm	kind	tiger
I will	behind	wild
I'll	remind	mild

long **i**, **ie**

pie	tie	die	cried
pies	tied	died	tried

A Spider in the Garden

The little spider peeked out of her egg sac. The air was mild. It seemed safe to go.

She crawled onto the grass. It was still wet from the rain. She did not mind. She wanted to be free.

The little spider crawled up a tall weed. She made a strand of silk and waited. The wind came, and she went up into the air. She felt wild and free as she sailed in the wind.

She landed behind an apple tree in a farmer's garden. She crawled up the tree and started to spin a web.

The spider made strands of silk with her legs. She pulled the strands out of her spinners. She stuck the ends of the strands to the tree. The little spider laid the silk strands on the web. At last, her trap was set. She hid behind a leaf and waited.

The spider waited until she
felt a tug on her web. Yes, a bug
was stuck to the silk. She bit the
bug and tied it up with strands of
silk. The bug made a big meal for
her.

The little spider was glad her web was in the farmer's garden. Lots of insects stuck in the web. The little spider got bigger and bigger.

And the farmer was glad to find the spider and her web in his garden. They helped get rid of the bugs that came to eat his plants.

At the end of summer, the spider made a silk egg sac. She kept the egg sac safe until winter passed.

At last summer came again. The big spider died. But the little spiders in the egg sac were safe.

One little spider peeked out of the egg sac. The air was mild. It seemed safe to go.

CHECK FOR UNDERSTANDING

1. How did the spider make a web?

2. Why was the farmer glad to see her?

long **i, i__e**

bike	like	line	kite
hike	alike	fine	bite
ride	side	dime	pile
wide	beside	time	mile
hide	inside	mine	smile
wire	hire	tire	fire

Garter Snakes

One day, Elaine went with her dad to a park. They hiked on a trail beside a small lake. He showed Elaine a lot of different trees and insects.

All of a sudden, Dad grabbed Elaine's hand and stopped. On a log near the water was a garter snake.

93

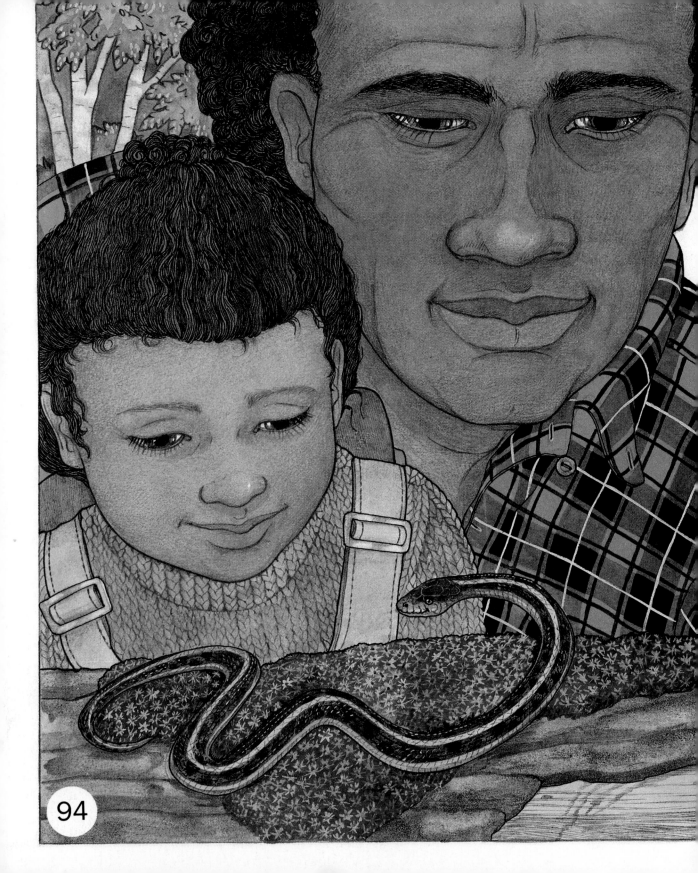

"Will it bite me?" asked Elaine.

"No," said her dad, "it will not bite you. Garter snakes are harmless snakes. Snakes like to lie in the sun to get warm. The three stripes tell you it is a garter snake."

Elaine bent down. She saw one stripe down the snake's back. She saw two stripes like lines down its sides.

"Can you see the little scales?" Dad asked. "The garter snake is a reptile. The skin of reptiles is made of scales."

Elaine wanted to feel the scales. She tried to pet the garter snake, but it crawled into the grass.

"Can I keep a garter snake as a pet?" asked Elaine.

"It will die unless it has frogs and insects to eat," said her dad.

"I can't get frogs and insects to feed a pet," she said. "A garter snake is better off in a park or a garden."

CHECK FOR UNDERSTANDING

1. Why was it OK to pet the snake?

2. Where is the best home for a garter snake? Why?

The Tiger and the Wild Plums

A little pink pig and her sister went out for a walk. They stopped beside the trail under a big, wild plum tree.

"The wild plums are ripe, said the little pink pig to her sister. "But we can't get up that tree."

A tiger went for a walk, too. The tiger saw the pigs and leaped onto the trail.

"Did I scare you?" the tiger asked the pigs.

"Not at all," said the little pink pig.

"I'm glad," said the tiger. "Is that a wild plum tree?"

"Yes, it is," said the little pink pig. "Will you pick plums for us?"

"Yes," he said. "I'll be glad to pick plums for all of us."

"How kind of you," said the two little pigs.

The tiger went up the tree. "The little pigs will eat the plums," he said to himself. "And they will get fatter and fatter. They will make a fine meal for me."

The little pink pig said to her sister, "We can trick the tiger."

"How?" asked her sister.

"The tiger will make the plums fall down," said the little pig. "But the plums will not be for the tiger. They will be for us to eat."

The little pink pig began to
hop up and down. "Tiger, Tiger!"
she called. "Pigs can hop up and
down. Can tigers?"

The big tiger saw the little
pigs hop up and down on the trail.
He tried to hop and keep the
plums in his paw.

The tiger hopped and hopped.
Plop, plop. Plop, plop, plop. All
the ripe plums fell down beside
the little pigs.

The pigs grabbed the plums
and ran down the trail.

"That was a fine trick," said
the sister to the little pink pig.

The tiger still hopped and hopped. He went up and down, up and down. And the little pigs had a fine meal of wild plums.

CHECK FOR UNDERSTANDING

1. Why did the tiger want the pigs to eat the plums?

2. How did the pigs trick him?

ir in **bird**

bird	fir	dirt	sir
girl	first	skirt	stir

The Hare and the Tortoise

The hare liked to brag. He liked to tell all the animals he was a fast runner.

One day the hare met a tortoise. The hare began to brag to him.

"I am a fast runner," he said to the tortoise. "I can run as fast as the wind."

The tortoise blinked and stared at the hare. "That *is* fast," the tortoise said.

"Well, you can't run at all," the hare went on. "You can't go as fast as I can."

The tortoise replied, "I admit I cannot run. I cannot go fast. But I walk a lot, and I do not stop. I will show you. Do you see that fir tree at the top of the hill? If we go on the dirt track, I'll get to the fir tree first."

"No, sir," said the hare. "I'm faster and I'll win. I'll get to the fir tree first. Get on the mark, get set, go!"

Off went the hare. Off went the tortoise. The hare ran fast down the dirt track and up the hill.

As the hare came near the fir tree, he stopped. He saw that the tortoise was still back at the bottom of the hill.

"I'm the fast one," said the hare. "I'll still be first. But for now, I'll stop for a little rest. I'll lie down beside the track and take a nap." And he did.

The tortoise plodded on and
on. He walked and walked and
walked. The tortoise was tired,
but he did not stop. At last he
came upon the hare, fast asleep
beside the track. The tortoise
grinned, passed the hare, and
walked on up the hill.

At last the hare got up. He
saw the tortoise near the top of
the hill. The hare ran as fast as
the wind, but it was too late. The
tortoise had stopped under the fir
tree. The tortoise had won.

"How did you win?" asked
the hare.

"You can go fast," said the
tortoise. "But you stopped and
slept beside the track. I walked
and did not stop. That is how I
got to the fir tree first."

After that, the hare was careful not to brag again.

CHECK FOR UNDERSTANDING

1. Where did the hare stop to rest? Why did he stop?

2. How did the tortoise get to the fir tree first?

PALS

Gail is a girl.
Sir is her dog.
The park is near.
They sit on a log.

Gail hears the the birds
and smells the trees.
She feels the sun.
That is how she sees.

Sir is her pal.
He sees for Gail.
What he cannot do
is read her braille.

Where Did It Happen?

1. Where did the hare take a nap?

2. Where did Elaine see a garter snake?

3. Where did the tiger hop?

4. Where did Deena Lake take the lost letter?

5. Where did the spider make a web?

6. Where did Ben sleep?

A TRIP TO TAKE

3

long **o, O o**

go	so	old	cold
no	sold	open	colt

gold	told	most	post
fold	hold	almost	October

Paco's Kindness

It was late October. The winter winds made Paco's farm cold.

"It will be warmer in the town inn," Paco told himself. "The town inn costs a lot, and I have no gold for the innkeeper. I will start out for town. Perhaps I will find kindness and help as I go."

And so Paco left for town. As he hiked down the lane, he met an old man. The man limped and struggled with a big sack on his back. He stumbled and almost fell.

"Old man," Paco cried, "you need a cane to help hold you up."

Paco cut a stick from a small tree at the side of the lane.

"Here is a cane for you, old man," he said.

"You are most kind," the man said to Paco. "You have made me a gift. Now I have a gift for you."

The old man put his hand into his sack. "Here is a big pot. Take it. And now I must go. Farewell."

A little later, Paco met a hunter. The hunter had made a fire at the side of the lane. He had a frown on his face. A dog sat beside him and howled.

"Hello," said Paco. "What is the matter?"

"I need a pot to put on the fire," the hunter grumbled. "Fido and I have not had a hot meal all week."

"I have a pot in my sack," said Paco. "I'll let you have it. I do not need it."

The hunter smiled. "How kind of you," he said. "But you must take a gift from me. Here is a blanket. Take it, please."

"Thank you," said Paco, and he bid the hunter farewell.

Later Paco met a lad and his colt. The lad had no cape, and he cried as he walked down the lane.

Paco asked, "What is the matter, lad?"

"Farmer!" cried the lad. "I have lost my cape, and I am so cold. I need a cape to keep me warm."

"I do not have a cape," Paco told the lad. "But I have a blanket. You can have it. I am not cold."

"You are most kind," said the lad. "But wait. You must take my colt as a gift."

Paco agreed to take the colt, and Paco bid the lad farewell.

Near the town, Paco came upon a maiden. She sat on an old rock wall.

"Farmer!" the maiden cried. "My feet are tired, and I have so far to walk. Can you help me?"

"Yes, you can have a ride into town with me," said Paco. "Get on the colt's back."

The maiden agreed and went into town with Paco on his colt.

"Thank you, farmer," she said. "You were so kind to me. Here is a gift for you."

The maiden handed Paco a little bag of gold. Paco held the gold in his hand and smiled.

"Now I can go to the town inn," he told himself. "I will be warm all winter! My small kindness to the old man has been well repaid."

CHECK FOR UNDERSTANDING

1. What was Paco's problem?

2. How was Paco kind to the people he met?

long **o, o__e**

note	hole	rode	home
nose	pole	rope	stone
rose	mole	hope	alone

o__e in **one**

one	come	someone
done	some	sometime

HOMER

Homer was little and fat. He was brown and had black stripes. Homer had lots of legs, feet, arms, and hands.

Homer liked to eat green plants. In the summer, he crawled up and down the tall blades of grass.

Homer had a home in the rose garden. His home was a little grass tunnel he made for himself.

Homer told Flo Mole that he liked to take a nap after his meals. She helped him print a note.

Flo and Homer tied the note to an old pole. Homer went into his little grass tunnel and had a fine nap.

PLEASE
DO NOT
WAKE UP
HOMER

But as Homer slept, it began to rain. It rained hard. Homer woke up. He was wet and cold. All his socks were wet. All his feet were cold. His nose was cold, too.

Homer tied a rope between two blades of grass. He pinned his socks to the line.

In the fall, it was time for
Homer to make a nest. He got up
on a twig and made a nest of fine
silk. Homer was safe and warm
inside his nest. All alone, Homer
slept and slept and slept.

In warm April, Homer woke up. He made a hole in his nest and crawled up onto the twig. He sat in the warm sun. He smiled. But Homer was not the same old Homer. Now he was a *mariposa*!

CHECK FOR UNDERSTANDING

1. Why did Homer make a silk nest?

2. What happened to Homer in the spring?

ROBOT, X-Y-2

Clink Clank Clink
    How do you do?
I'm little Robot
    X-Y-2.

I can make beds
    and scrub and sweep,
And do it with
    a beep, beep, beep.

140

Can I feed dogs and cats?
     You bet!
And I can get
     the table set.

So if you want
     a helper too,
Put in a call
     to X-Y-2.

or

or	for	corn	forest
order	fork	corner	florist

ore

more	core	tore	sore
wore	score	store	before

A Trip to the Florist

Kim's mom, Mrs. Lee, is a florist. She sells plants and flowers. Her store is on the corner of First Street. Sometimes Kim and I go to her store.

The store is like a forest. It is filled with small trees in tubs. Big ferns are in pots and baskets. In the back are flowers and plants of all kinds.

Mrs. Lee was born in Korea. Her mom showed her how to take care of flowers. Now Mrs. Lee shows Kim and me.

Mrs. Lee tells us the names of all the flowers in the store. We help Mrs. Lee water all the flowers and green plants.

She shows us how to put flowers in paper and tie on a ribbon.

Customers come from far and near. Last week a man came into the store from Oregon. He wanted to order flowers for his little girl.

"How old is she?" asked Mrs. Lee.

"She will be ten," said the man.

Mrs. Lee sold him ten pink roses.

One day Mr. Horner came into the store from across town. He had ordered plants from Kim's mom before. The plants did well, so Mr. Horner came back to get more.

Mrs. Lee sold him one tall cactus and two small, fat cactus plants.

"Remember," she said,
"cactus plants like sun, but not
a lot of water."

Later, a gardener came into
the store for flower seeds. She
wanted to plant flowers for her
customers.

147

I like to meet the customers.
I like to take care of the plants.
I like to see and smell the flowers,
too. I hope someday I can be
a florist.

CHECK FOR UNDERSTANDING

1. How did the girls help Kim's mom?

2. How did Kim's mom get to be a florist?

POPCORN

Popcorn is a snack most of us like. It is not the same as sweet corn or corn-on-the-cob.

You can't eat popcorn until it is popped. An ear of popcorn is small. Its kernels are small and hard. But the corn inside is soft and damp.

What makes popcorn pop? First you have to get the kernels hot. The heat makes steam inside the kernel. The steam makes the kernel open.

P-O-P! The soft corn inside puffs up, and it's POPCORN.

You can add salt or butter. Popcorn is better for us if we eat it plain.

Lots of us eat popcorn at a show. But most popcorn is made and eaten at home.

It is fun to pop corn at a campfire.

You can make ropes with popped corn. Put the ropes outside in the winter to feed the birds.

long **o, oa**

oak	boat	road	soap
soak	coat	toad	float
croak	goat	load	toast

oa with **r**

oar   roar

long **o, oe**

toe	toes
hoe	goes

HOMESICK

Hope was tired of the rain. It seemed to rain all the time at camp. Hope liked camp, but she felt sad. No one was in the tent with her, and she felt lonesome.

Hope sat on her cot. She wanted to send a note home. She wanted Dad to come and get her.

The rain came down harder.
The wind roared in the trees. The
storm was bad. Hail hit the top of
the tent. Water dripped on Hope's
nose, and raindrops hit her hand.

Emma came into Hope's tent.

"I have some mail for you," she said. Emma slipped off her backpack.

"Here is a letter, and you have a postcard, too," Emma said.

Hope opened
the letter first.
It was from her
little sister, Kate.

Dear Hope,
Last week I started a garden.
Mom helped me dig up the dirt.
I planted some carrots and some beans.
I put in six tomato plants.
A brown toad has made his home in my garden.
He hopped on Mom's toe, and she almost hopped on him, too!
How do you like summer at camp?
I miss you!
I'll keep a tomato or two for you.
X X X Kate

Hope felt better. Her sister,
Kate, missed her. The rain had
stopped. Hope picked up her pen
and her note pad.

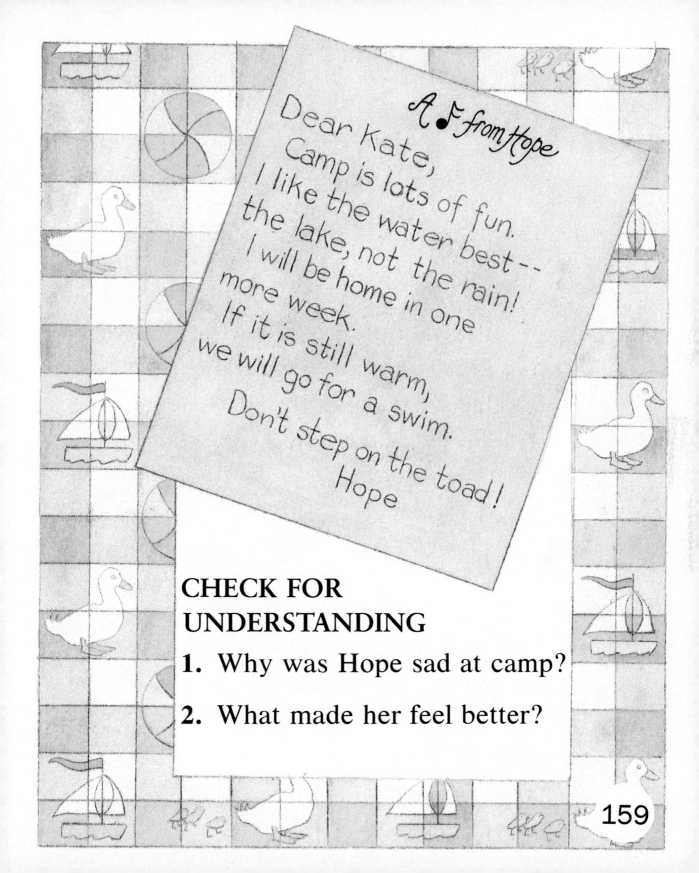

A ♪ F from Hope

Dear Kate,
Camp is lots of fun.
I like the water best --
the lake, not the rain!
I will be home in one
more week.
If it is still warm,
we will go for a swim.
Don't step on the toad!
Hope

CHECK FOR UNDERSTANDING

1. Why was Hope sad at camp?

2. What made her feel better?

A Goat in a Boat

I saw an old goat,
Oh, I saw an old goat
Down at the oak tree
In a red coat.

I saw an old goat,
Oh, I saw an old goat.
He went down the road
To pick up a note.

I saw an old goat,
Oh, I saw an old goat
Get in a tub
And set it afloat.

Did you see the old goat
In his red coat
Go down the road
Pick up the note
Get in the tub
Set it afloat?
Did you see the old goat?
NO!

J j

jam	jar	junk	joke
jacks	jaw	jump	jeep
jacket	job	just	jerk

162

Pedro's Find

Pedro liked rocks a lot. He kept his rocks in jars. He had jars at home, all filled to the top.

Pedro's dad liked to tease him.

"Here is a jam jar for more junk," he said. "You and Ana are just alike. You like rocks best of all."

Ana is Pedro's big sister. Ana's job is to collect rocks. She finds and sorts the rocks.

"Pedro," she said, "I want to find some rock samples. Do you want to come with me?"

"Yes!" cried Pedro. "Will we go to the mine? Do I need my hard hat?"

"No," said Ana, "not today. The rocks I need today are near the big cliff."

Pedro grabbed his jacket and backpack, and they started out.

Pedro sat beside Ana in the jeep. They went down an old dirt road. It had lots of deep holes in it. The jeep bumped and jerked from side to side. They stopped at the bottom of the cliff.

"Here we are at last," said Ana. "I hope I can find the rocks I need."

Ana filled her bag with all kinds of rocks. Pedro picked up some rocks to take home, too. He had almost filled his backpack.

"Ana, Ana," he called.

"What do you want?" she asked.

"Come and see!" said Pedro. "I picked up a funny rock."

Ana ran to see what Pedro had in his hand.

"It is an old, old rock," she said. "I wonder if it is the jaw bone of a bird. Take care of it until we get home."

Back at home, Pedro showed the funny rock to his dad.

"Oh, no! Not more junk," he said as he smiled at Pedro.

"Dad, it's not just a rock," Pedro told his dad. "Ana said it is the jaw bone of a bird. It is so old it's like a rock now. Ana said it's called a *fossil*."

"Wow!" said his dad. "You will hear no more rock jokes from me."

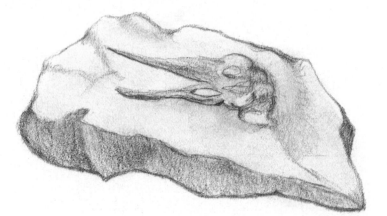

CHECK FOR UNDERSTANDING

1. Why did Pedro's dad like to tease him?

2. Where did Pedro find a fossil?

ROCKS

by Florence Parry Heide

Big rocks into pebbles
Pebbles into sand.
I really hold a million million rocks
here in my hand.

V v

van	gave	cave	five
vest	wave	save	dive
visit	pave	stove	drive

alive	over
arrive	river

more words with v

give	love	have
live	glove	move

The Little Silver Robot

A golden beam lit up the dark forest. Out from the beam came a little silver robot. The robot blinked and jerked his feet. He had arrived. His visit had begun.

"Now if I can just find a man," the little robot said to himself. "The big silver robots said a man will speak to me. I have to find a man before I can go back home."

173

The robot moved his silver legs and arms until he came to a cave.

"Perhaps I will find a man in here," said the robot. "I'll go in and see."

Inside the cave was a big black stove. The little robot walked over to it. He spoke to the stove. But the stove didn't speak to him.

On a nail near the stove was an old brown coat. Near it was a vest. The robot spoke to the coat and the vest. But they didn't speak to him.

"I must go on and hunt for a man," the robot said.

He moved his little legs in
jerks until he came to a small
lake. A duck swam and dived in
the water. The duck went up into
the air. At last, the duck came
back down and landed on the lake
again.

The robot went over and
spoke to the duck. *The duck
spoke to the robot!*

"Now I can go home!" the
little silver robot said with a big
grin.

Back home, the little robot went to see the big silver robots.

"Tell us," said the most important robot. "Did the man speak to you?"

"Yes," said the little robot. "The man spoke to me."

"Is a man just like us?" she asked.

"Noooo!" said the little robot. "I saw a man swim and dive in a lake. I saw a man go up into the air. I saw him land on water. And the man spoke to me!"

"Fine job!" said all the big robots.

CHECK FOR UNDERSTANDING

1. Where did the little robot hunt for a man?

2. What did he tell the big robots?

Hidden Gold

Patrick O'Dee got up at dawn to do his job. Patrick's job was to keep up the fire at home. Patrick and his five sisters lived near a forest in Ireland.

Patrick put a big sack over his back and went into the forest. He picked up some fir cones, twigs, and bits of bark. Patrick filled his sack and started down the trail for home.

All of a sudden, Patrick stopped. He was not alone in the forest.

Patrick peeked from behind a tree. He saw a little man come down the trail. Patrick stared at him. The little man wore a tall black hat and a green coat and vest. The little man was an elf.

"An elf has a pot of gold," Patrick said to himself. "If I can grab the elf, I can have his gold."

He waited behind the tree. As
the elf passed, Patrick jumped
onto the trail and grabbed him.

"Let me go! Let me go!"
screamed the elf, as he jumped up
and down.

"I will let you go," said
Patrick. "But first you must
promise to give me a pot of gold.
And no tricks!"

At last the elf agreed. "I will take you to a pot of gold if you will let me go free."

The elf led Patrick down a steep trail into the dark forest. The elf stopped. He put his hand on the trunk of a big tree.

"The pot of gold is here,
under the tree," he said. "Now
you must set me free."

"But I have no shovel to dig
up the gold," Patrick complained.

"You will just have to get
one," said the elf. "Now you
must keep the promise you made
and let me go."

"I will," said Patrick. "But first I will tie my scarf to the tree. You must promise not to take it off."

"I promise I will not take the scarf off the tree," said the elf. "But you must go now. Do not come back until dawn."

Patrick tied his scarf onto the tree.

"I'll get a shovel and come back at dawn," he said. "My scarf will mark the spot to dig for the gold."

At dawn Patrick came back to dig up the gold. But all the trees were just alike! Tree, after tree, after tree had the same scarf tied on it.

Patrick dug and dug until dark. At last he gave up and went home. The little elf had kept his promise . . . *and* his pot of gold.

CHECK FOR UNDERSTANDING

1. Why did Patrick grab the elf?

2. How did the elf trick Patrick?

UNIT REVIEW

What Happened Next?

Homesick

1.

2.

3.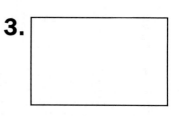

What happened next?

The Little Silver Robot

1.

2.

3.

What happened next?

Homer

1.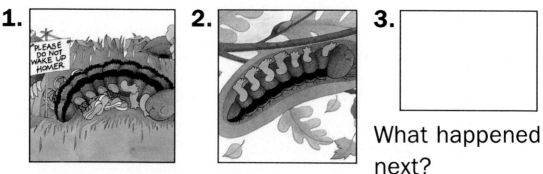

2.

3.

What happened next?

Hidden Gold

1. 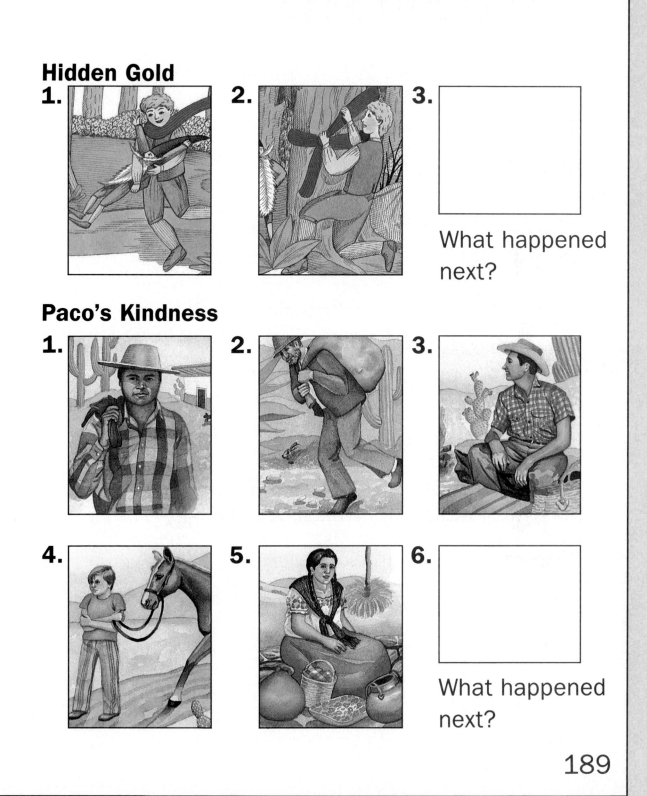 **2.** **3.**

What happened next?

Paco's Kindness

1. **2.** **3.**

4. **5.** **6.**

What happened next?

Story Vocabulary